# *The Organ Music of Malcolm Archer*

# The Organ Music of Malcolm Archer

*Twenty-five characteristic pieces*

Kevin Mayhew

We hope you enjoy *The Organ Music of Malcolm Archer.*
Further copies of this and our many other books are available
from your local music shop or Christian bookshop.

In case of difficulty, please contact the publisher direct by writing to:

The Sales Department
KEVIN MAYHEW LTD
Rattlesden
Bury St Edmunds
Suffolk IP30 0SZ

Phone 01449 737978
Fax 01449 737834

Please ask for our complete catalogue of outstanding Church Music.

Front Cover: *The Garden of the Peaceful Arts* by Lorenzo Costa (*c.*1460-1535).
Courtesy of the Louvre, Paris/Bridgeman Art Library, London.
Reproduced by kind permission.

Cover designed by Graham Johnstone and Veronica Ward.

# Contents

# About the Composer

MALCOLM ARCHER (*b.*1952) is one of the more prolific of English composers for the church, with over a hundred works published. He studied at the Royal College of Music and was Organ Scholar at Jesus College, Cambridge. Since then, he has held appointments at Norwich and Bristol Cathedrals and is currently Organist and Master of the Choristers at Wells Cathedral. He is conductor of the Wells Oratorio Society and the City of Bristol Choir.

In addition to his work as a composer and conductor, he leads a busy life as an organ recitalist and has played all over the world, broadcast on B.B.C. Radio and produced numerous recordings.

# FESTIVE SCHERZO

Malcolm Archer (*b*.1952)

Sw. *mf*

– Gt. to Ped.

*poco rall.*

*a tempo*

Gt. *f*

+Gt. to Ped.

# DRAW NEAR WITH FAITH ✓

## Malcolm Archer

**Un poco adagio** (♩ = 50)

# PRELUDE ON 'NOEL NOUVELET'

Malcolm Archer

# COMMUNION

Malcolm Archer

# ELEGY

## Malcolm Archer

# PAGEANT

Malcolm Archer

22

Sw. Reeds *mp legato*

24

# SICILIENNE

Malcolm Archer (*b.*1952)

**With a gentle lilt** (♪ = 132)

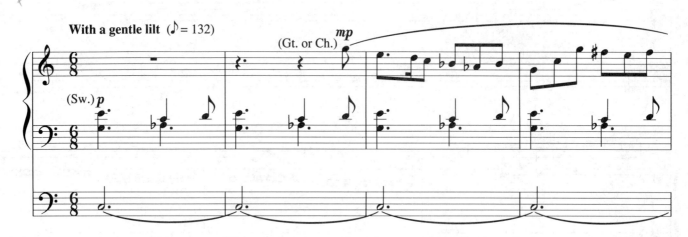

*poco rall.*

27

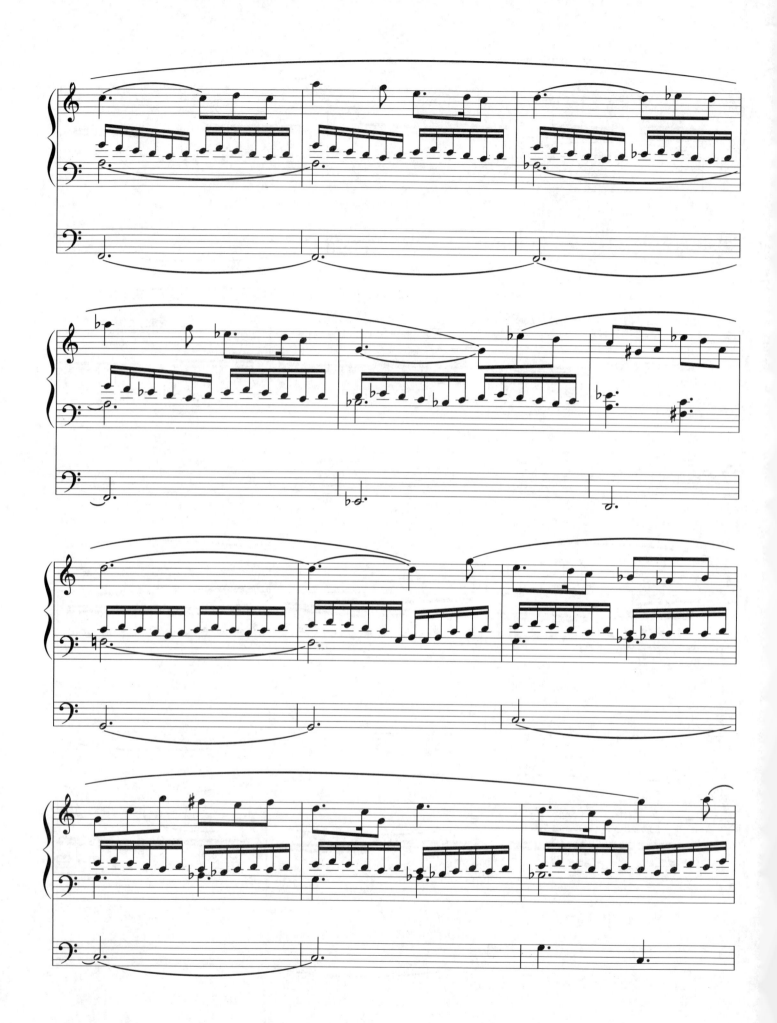

31

# A PASCHAL FANFARE

## Malcolm Archer

Vivace (♩ = 104)

2nd time to Coda

Tuba

33

37

# PRELUDE ON 'HUMILITY'

Malcolm Archer

# AN EVENING LITANY ✓

Malcolm Archer

# CARILLON

Malcolm Archer

**Con moto** (♩ = 120)

# ENGLISH COUNTRY GARDENS

## Malcolm Archer

# THE DOVE DESCENDING

Malcolm Archer

Slow (♩ = 69)

Ch. 8' 1' (or tierce)

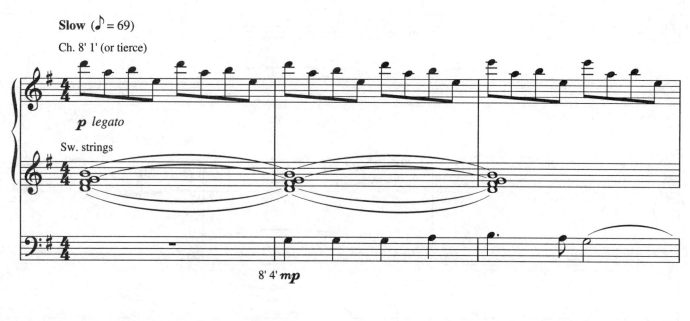

*p* legato

Sw. strings

8' 4' *mp*

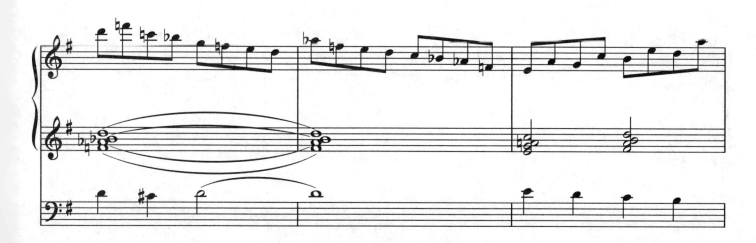

rall. poco a poco

dim.

ppp

32'

51

# PRELUDE ON 'AUS DER TIEFE'

Malcolm Archer

*For Martin Schellenberg*

# ALLA MARCIA

### Malcolm Archer

last time to Coda

57

# √ GREENSLEEVES (Bluesleeves)

### Malcolm Archer

61

# CANTILENE
Malcolm Archer (*b*.1952)

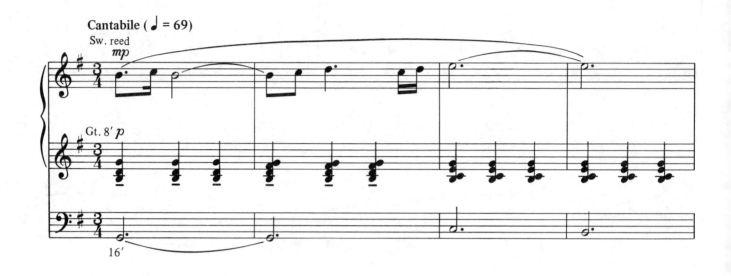

**Tempo I**

Sw. (8′ reed) (– Sw. to Gt.)

Gt. 8′      *sim.*

*poco rall.*

# PRELUDE ON 'DOMINUS REGIT ME'

Malcolm Atcher

71

# PRELUDE ON 'ST MAGNUS'

Malcolm Archer

73

*For Robert Hall and the Centenary of the organ at Thornbury Church*

# A THORNBURY FANFARE

## Malcolm Archer

*For R.J.W.*

# A CAPTIVATING CAPRICE

Malcolm Archer

80

81

# PRELUDE ON 'ALL FOR JESUS'

Malcolm Archer

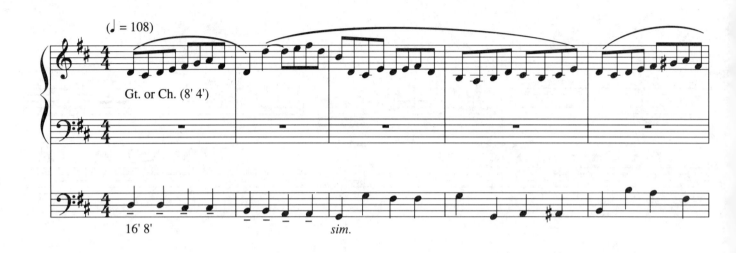

# INTERMEZZO

Malcolm Archer

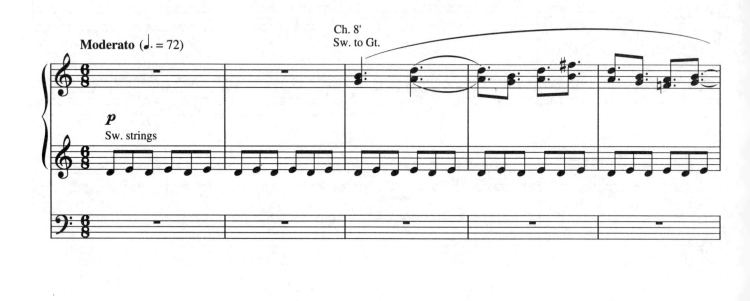

85

Gt.

Gt. to Ped.

86

# DANCE SCHERZO

Malcolm Archer

last time to Coda

Gt.

90

D.S. al Coda ⊕ CODA

# FESTIVAL FINALE

Malcolm Archer